This book belongs to

. . . . . . . . . . . . . . . . . . . . . . . . . . . . .

# DRESS-UP
## ❧ Day ❧

Can you find
a Ladybird on
every page?

by Mary Atkinson

make
believe
ideas

# Get the most from this reader

**Before reading:**

● Look at the pictures and discuss them together. Ask questions such as, "What type of pet is this?"

● Relate the topic to your child's world. For example, say: "What pets do we have?"

● Familiarise your child with book vocabulary by using terms such as *word, letter, title, author* and *text.*

**During reading:**

● Prompt your child to sound out unknown words. Draw attention to neglected middle or end sounds.

● Encourage your child to use the pictures as clues to unknown words.

● Occasionally, ask what might happen next, and then check together as you read on.

- Monitor your child's understanding. Repeated readings can improve fluency and comprehension.

- Keep reading sessions short and enjoyable. Stop if your child becomes tired or frustrated.

• • • • • • • • • • • • • • • • • • • • • • • • • • • • • • •

**After reading:**

- Discuss the book. Encourage your child to form opinions with questions such as, "What did you like best about this book?"

- Help your child work through the fun activities at the back of the book. Then ask him or her to reread the story. Praise any improvement.

Some pets can fly
across the sky.

Some pets can smile and sing.

9

Some pets are wearing giant glasses.

Some pets are wearing wings.

Some pets look like scary pirates.

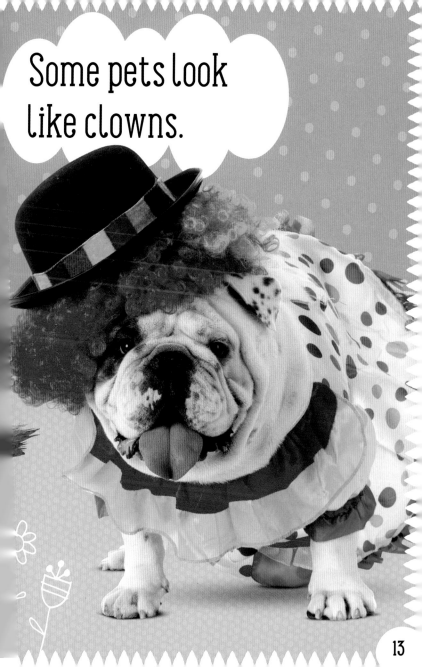

Some pets look
like clowns.

Some pets are wearing cosy hats.

Some pets are wearing crowns.

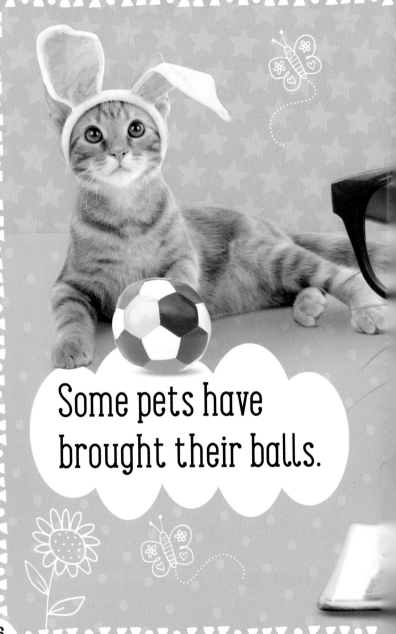

Some pets have
brought their balls.

Some pets have brought their books.

Some pets can drive very fast.

Some pets are clever cooks.

Some pets like wearing yellow.

Some pets like wearing gre

All the pets are having fun . . .

because it's dress-up day!

# Discussion Questions

**1** Which pet is wearing a crown?

**2** Which pet likes music?

**3** What would you like to dress up as? Why?

# ❧ Sight Words ❧

Learning sight words helps you read fluently. Practise these sight words from the book. Use them in sentences of your own.

can

their

look

fly

are

some

like

sing

# ❧ Rhyming Words ❧

Can you find the rhyming pairs?
Say them aloud.

thing

hat

day

bat

lay

sing

# Writing Practice

Read the words, and then trace them with your finger.

smile

giant

crown

scary

wings

clever

# ✑ Silly Sentences ✑

Have fun filling in the gap in each sentence. Use the ideas below or make up your own.

Some pets can ............................ .

ome pets like eating ......................... .